Social Studies Alive!®
Regions of Our Country

Chief Executive Officer: Bert Bower

Chief Operating Officer: Amy Larson

Director of Product Development: Liz Russell

Managing Editor: Laura Alavosus

Editorial Project Manager: Lara Fox

Project Editors: Wendy Frey and Nancy O'Leary

Editorial Associates: Anna Embree and Sarah Sudano

Production Manager: Lynn Sanchez

Design Manager: Jeff Kelly

Graphic Designer: Victoria Philp

Photo Edit Manager: Margee Robinson

Photo Editor: Diane Austin

Art Editors: Eric Houts and Sarah Wildfang

Audio Manager: Katy Haun

Teachers' Curriculum Institute
P.O. Box 50996
Palo Alto, CA 94303

Customer Service: 800-497-6138
www.teachtci.com

ISBN 978-1-58371-852-0

1 2 3 4 5 6 7 8 9 10 -QW- 15 14 13 12 11 10 09

Acknowledgments

Program Director

Bert Bower

Program Consultant

Vicki LaBoskey, Ph.D., Professor of Education, Mills College, Oakland, California

Student Edition Writers

Susan Buckley

Diane Hanover

Diane Hart

Peter Lacey

Curriculum Developers

Joyce Bartky

Anne Maloney

Elizabeth Sarica

Steve Seely

Kelly Shafksy

Reading Specialist

Barbara Schubert, Ph.D., Reading Specialist, Saint Mary's College, Moraga, California

Teacher and Content Consultants

Lynn Casey, Teacher, Husmann Elementary School, Crystal Lake, Illinois

Jane Crowe, Teacher, Brookwood Elementary School, Tuscaloosa County, Alabama

Khieta Davis, Teacher, Flower City School #54, Rochester, New York

Ann Dawson, Educational Consultant, Intermediate Curriculum Specialist, Gahanna, Ohio

Shirley Jacobs, Library Media Specialist, Irving Elementary School, Bloomington, Illinois

Elizabeth McKenna, Teacher, St. Thomas Aquinas Catholic School, Diocese of Orlando, Florida

Mitch Pascal, Social Studies Specialist, Arlington County Schools, Arlington, Virginia

Becky Suthers, Retired Teacher, Stephen F. Austin Elementary, Weatherford, Texas

Tiffany Wilson, Teacher, Corbell Elementary, Frisco, Texas

Literature Consultant

Regina M. Rees, Ph.D., Assistant Professor, Beeghly College of Education, Youngstown State University, Youngstown, Ohio

Music Specialist

Beth Yankee, Teacher, The Woodward School for Technology and Research, Kalamazoo, Michigan

Maps

Mapping Specialists, Ltd., Madison, Wisconsin

Contents

Contents

For each subject, write a sentence that answers this question:
Why is this subject important to us?

Subject 1: Math

Subject 2: Science

Subject 3: Social Studies

Subject 4: Language Arts

—

1

Read Sections 1.2 through 1.5 in your book. After reading each section, decorate the hat that matches that social scientist. Write words and draw symbols and pictures to tell what each social scientist does.

1.2 Economist

1.3 Geographer

1.4 Political Scientist

1.5 Historian

1

Picture yourself as an archaeologist 500 years from now. Carefully examine the artifacts in front of you. Then write a detailed description of four artifacts. Use the following questions to help you describe each artifact:

- What materials do you think the artifact is made of?
- Is the artifact large or small?
- Is it worn or broken, or is it in good shape?
- What might someone in the future think this object was used for?

Artifact 1	Artifact 2
Artifact 3	Artifact 4

What conclusions might an archaeologist draw about how the makers of the artifacts lived?

Complete one of the following four activities. Use one of the Extra Student Work pages at the back of your Interactive Student Notebook.

Economist Activity

Write a short story about a time when you earned money on your own. Illustrate your story.

Geographer Activity

Decide which state you might like to live in when you are an adult. Draw a map of the state. Under the map, explain your reasons.

Political Scientist Activity

Write a note to your principal in which you suggest an improvement to your school grounds. In your note, explain to the principal why your opinion should matter.

Historian Activity

Create a timeline of your mother's, father's, or guardian's past. Draw a horizontal line from left to right to represent the person's life. Draw short vertical (up-and-down) lines to show when an important event happened (like the day someone was born). Put the events in the order in which they happened, with the first one farthest to the left. Include at least five events that most explain who the person is today. Draw a symbol for each event on the timeline.

Dad
was
born

Dad
married
Mom

2

Create a map of your home as if you were looking down on it from above. Label each room. Then, divide your home into five regions and make each region a different color. Last, answer the question, *What sets each region apart from the rest of the house?*

2

Follow the directions on the Geography Challenge cards.
Use your Interactive Desk Map to help you.

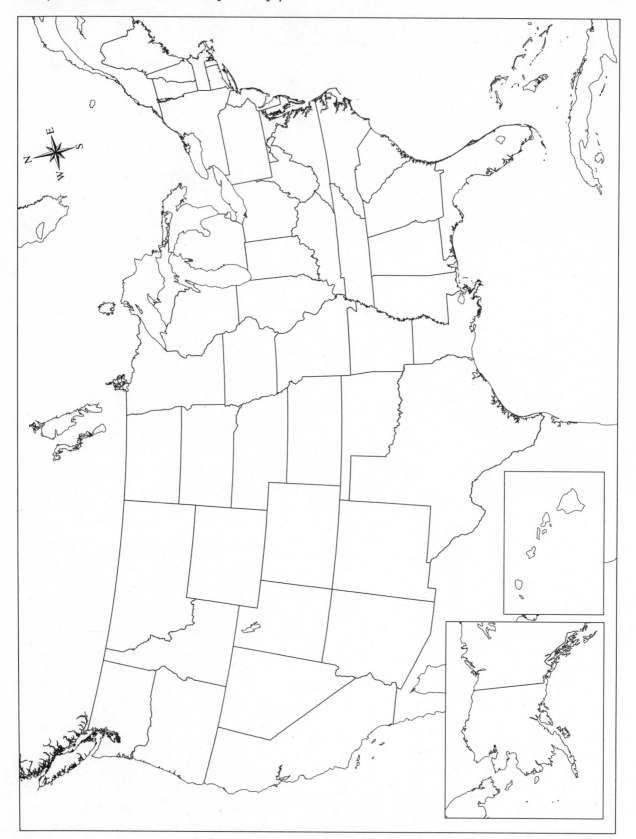

Answer each Geography Challenge 2B card in the correct space below.

Question 1

Question 2

Question 3

Question 4

Question 5

Question 6

Question 7

Question 8

Question 9

Question 10

2

Write the name of the city or physical landmark that you and your partner think the photograph shows. Explain your reasons.

1. We think Transparency 2E is a photograph of

2. We think Transparency 2F is a photograph of

3. We think Transparency 2G is a photograph of

4. We think Transparency 2H is a photograph of

5. We think Transparency 2I is a photograph of

Use the map below to help you and your partner ask and answer questions about the Mississippi River.

Questions

Write three questions to ask another pair. For example: *How many states does the Mississippi River run through?*

1.

2.

3.

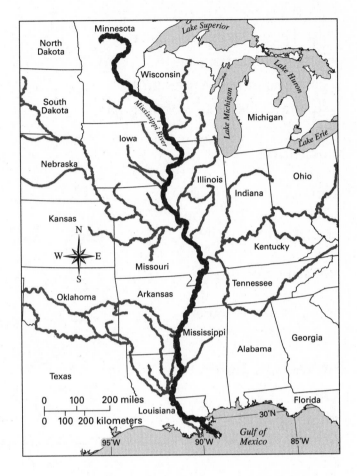

Answers

Write the answers to three questions another pair asks you.

1.

2.

3.

2 Choose three locations around the United States that you would like to visit. For each location,

- list the exact latitude and longitude.
- list the average annual rainfall.
- list the population density.
- list the approximate elevation.
- draw a simple picture of the location.

Location 1

Latitude and longitude   _____

Average annual rainfall   _____

Population density   _____

Approximate elevation   _____

Location 2

Latitude and longitude   _____

Average annual rainfall   _____

Population density   _____

Approximate elevation   _____

Location 3

Latitude and longitude   _____

Average annual rainfall   _____

Population density   _____

Approximate elevation   _____

3

Suppose the following things were no longer a part of your life.
In the box below, draw the one thing you would miss the most.
Then write a paragraph explaining your choice.

- drums
- ballet
- martial arts
- tacos
- jewelry

The One Thing I Would Miss the Most

Why I Would Miss This the Most

3

For each group of Americans, read and follow the directions.

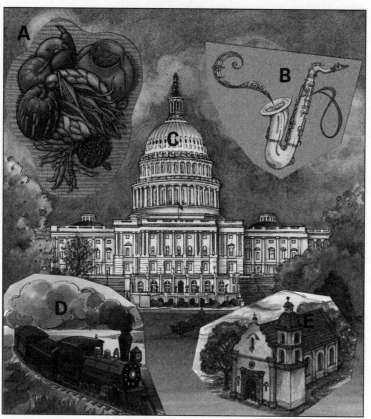

American Indians

Make a simple sketch to represent this group's settlement experience.

Write one sentence to describe this group's settlement experience.

Look at the collage. Write the letter of this group's contribution: _____

Latinos

Make a simple sketch to represent this group's settlement experience.

Write one sentence to describe this group's settlement experience.

Look at the collage. Write the letter of this group's contribution: _____

European Americans

Make a simple sketch to represent this group's settlement experience.

Write one sentence to describe this group's settlement experience.

Look at the collage. Write the letter of this group's contribution: _____

3

African Americans

Make a simple sketch to represent this group's settlement experience.

Write one sentence to describe this group's settlement experience.

Look at the collage. Write the letter of this group's contribution: _____

Asian Americans

Make a simple sketch to represent this group's settlement experience.

Write one sentence to describe this group's settlement experience.

Look at the collage. Write the letter of this group's contribution: _____

3

History Detective Assignment: Where did the early settlers in your neighborhood come from?

Write one paragraph telling what you discovered.

Write one paragraph telling how you found this information.

3

Write five new verses for the song "This Land Is Your Land." Your verses must be about the five groups you studied in this lesson: American Indians, Latinos, European Americans, African Americans, and Asian Americans. The verses should contain information about where each group came from and the contributions each group has made to American society.

This Land Is Your Land

This land is your land, this land is my land,

From California to the New York Island,

From the redwood forest to the Gulf Stream waters,

This land was made for you and me.

Verse 1
They came from

Verse 2
They came from

Verse 3
They came from

Verse 4
They came from

Verse 5
They came from

Examine each of the places shown in the collage of the Northeast.
Also look at the map in Section 4.1 of your book to see the places
where the tour will stop. If you could take a trip to any one place
in the Northeast, which one would you most want to visit? Why?
Write your answer below.

My Northeast Trip

4

Use the spaces below to answer the questions on the Geography Challenge Cards. Write complete sentences. Then, on the map, draw and label the feature that answers each question. Exchange your question with another pair of students until you have completed all the cards.

Question 1.

Question 2.

Question 3.

Question 4.

Question 5.

Question 6.

Question 7.

Question 8.

Question 9.

Question 10.

4

Your class is taking a train tour of the Northeast region. The tour will take you to nine locations. As you move from site to site, draw a line on the map to show your route. After visiting each site, draw a symbol or an image at that location to show what you learned there.

Suppose you are a newspaper reporter. You want to write about the
working conditions in the Lowell mills. Write at least five questions
to ask a mill worker in an interview. Then write the answers that
you think the mill worker would give.

Reporter:

Mill Worker:

Reporter:

Mill Worker:

Reporter:

Mill Worker:

Reporter:

Mill Worker:

Reporter:

Mill Worker:

Look closely at the image your teacher has projected. With your partner, discuss and record answers to the questions below.

What do the bright areas on this photograph of the United States represent? What do the dark areas represent?

In which half of the country do more people live, the East or the West? Why do you think this might be so?

There is a concentration of lights in the Northeast. Compare this image with the large U.S. map on your Interactive Desk Map, which shows some of the cities of the Northeast. Which large cities are bunched together along the Northeast coast of the United States?

5

Read Sections 5.4 through 5.8.
Record notes in the appropriate spaces.

Life in the Northeast Megalopolis

5.4 Housing

5.5 Employment

5.6 Transportation

5.7 Environment

5.8 Recreation

Life in a Small Northeastern Town

5.4 Housing

5.5 Employment

5.6 Transportation

5.7 Environment

5.8 Recreation

5

1. Briefly explain how these inventions changed city life.

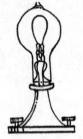

Electricity changed city life in this way:

The automobile changed city life in this way:

2. Draw a picture of something you could invent to solve one problem of living in a densely populated city. Look at the following list for ideas:
   - places to live
   - getting around
   - people and pollution

5

Create a simple comic strip about life in the Northeast.
Follow these steps:

- Give your comic strip a title. Enter your name as the author.

- Create two characters. One is from the megalopolis. The other is from a farm and has never visited a large city. Draw sketches of the two characters in the four frames of the cartoon. Put any words the characters say in speech bubbles.

- In your cartoon, mention at least two of these topics: *housing, employment, transportation, the environment,* and *recreation.*

Title: By:	

Look carefully at the collage of the Southeast that your teacher (Pg85) has projected. Also look at the map in Section 6.1 of your book to see the places where the tour will stop. If you could take a trip to any one place in the Southeast, which one would you most want to visit? Why? Write your answer below.

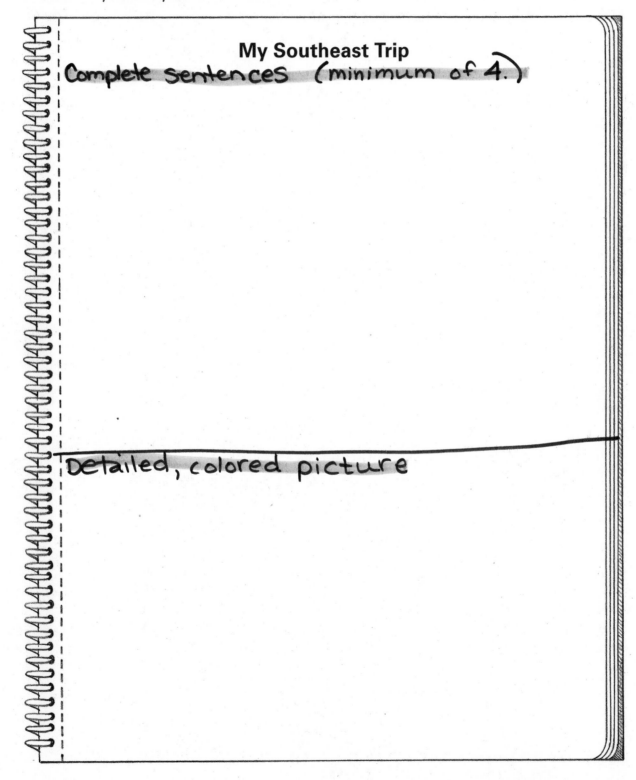

My Southeast Trip

Complete sentences (minimum of 4.)

Detailed, colored picture

6

Follow these steps to complete each card:
Use the spaces below to answer the questions on the
Geography Challenge Cards. Write complete sentences.
Then, on the map, draw and label the feature that answers
each question. Exchange your question with another pair
of students until you have completed all the cards.

Question 1.

Question 2.

Question 3.

Question 4.

Question 5.

Question 6.

Question 7.

6

Step 1: You will create a quilt square for the class quilt. Select five pieces of patterned paper and three pieces of solid paper from the scraps your teacher will provide. You may tear or cut your paper if you want. Use your materials to create an abstract design. Then paste your design onto the paper square your teacher will give you.

Step 2: When your teacher calls your name, place your finished square next to your classmates' squares, as if in a quilt.

Step 3: Look at the quilt the class has created. Answer the following questions in writing:

1. What pattern or patterns do you see in the quilt as a whole? Describe the pattern(s).

2. Quilts tell us something about the people who made them. What do you think this quilt might tell people about your class?

3. Quilts tell us something about the places in which they are made. What do you think this quilt might tell people about the place where you live?

Draw two pieces of clothing that Robert will need to wear when he goes outside for recess in the winter.

7

How does geography affect life in the Southeast? Investigate for yourself. For each placard, follow the four steps in the corresponding box on the following pages.

Placard 7A: Geography Investigation: Elevation in the Southeast

Step 1: Draw an arrow from this box to the geography feature in the illustration that best matches the map on the wall.

Step 2: Write your hypothesis (educated guess) to Geography Investigation Question 4.

Step 3: Read Section 7.2 in *Social Studies Alive! Regions of Our Country.* Is your hypothesis mentioned in the book? Circle *yes* or *no.*   Yes   No

Step 4: Write one effect that elevation has on the Southeast region.

Placard 7B: Geography Investigation: Rivers and Ocean of the Southeast

Step 1: Draw an arrow from this box to the geography feature in the illustration that best matches the map on the wall.

Step 2: Write your hypothesis (educated guess) to Geography Investigation Question 4.

Step 3: Read Section 7.3 in *Social Studies Alive! Regions of Our Country*. Is your hypothesis mentioned in the book? Circle *yes* or *no*.   Yes   No

Step 4: Write one effect that the rivers and the ocean have on the Southeast region.

Placard 7C: Geography Investigation: The Fall Line in the Southeast

Step 1: Draw an arrow from this box to the geography feature in the illustration that best matches the map on the wall.

Step 2: Write your hypothesis (educated guess) to Geography Investigation Question 4.

Step 3: Read Section 7.4 in *Social Studies Alive! Regions of Our Country*. Is your hypothesis mentioned in the book? Circle *yes* or *no*.   Yes   No

Step 4: Write one effect that the fall line has on the Southeast region.

7

Placard 7D: Geography Investigation: Natural Resources of the Southeast

Step 1: Draw an arrow from this box to the geography feature in the illustration that best matches the map on the wall.

Step 2: Write your hypothesis (educated guess) to Geography Investigation Question 4.

Step 3: Read Section 7.6 in *Social Studies Alive! Regions of Our Country.* Is your hypothesis mentioned in the book? Circle *yes* or *no.*   Yes   No

Step 4: Write one effect that natural resources have on the Southeast region.

Placard 7E: Geography Investigation: Growing Seasons in the Southeast

Step 1: Draw an arrow from this box to the geography feature in the illustration that best matches the map on the wall.

Step 2: Write your hypothesis (educated guess) to Geography Investigation Question 4.

Step 3: Read Section 7.6 in *Social Studies Alive! Regions of Our Country.*
Is your hypothesis mentioned in the book? Circle *yes* or *no.*   Yes   No

Step 4: Write one effect that the lengthy growing season has on the Southeast region.

Placard 7F: Geography Investigation: Dangerous Weather in the Southeast

Step 1: Draw an arrow from this box to the geography feature in the illustration that best matches the map on the wall.

Step 2: Write your hypothesis (educated guess) to Geography Investigation Question 4.

Step 3: Read Section 7.7 in *Social Studies Alive! Regions of Our Country.*
Is your hypothesis mentioned in the book? Circle *yes* or *no.*   Yes   No

Step 4: Write one effect that weather events have on the Southeast region.

7

Step 1: Suppose that you are a reporter for a newspaper. Your assignment is to interview people in Florida who experienced Hurricane Andrew. Write three important questions that you would want to ask these people, to find out how Hurricane Andrew affected their lives.

1.

2.

3.

Step 2: Now suppose that you lived in Florida when Hurricane Andrew hit. Using what you learned from your reading, answer the three questions above.

1.

2.

3.

Step 3: Write a one-paragraph newspaper story on the effect Hurricane Andrew had on Florida. Make up a quotation from someone who survived the storm. Give your article a catchy title.

Select three of the geography topics you have just studied: climate, elevation, natural resources, or bodies of water such as rivers, lakes, and oceans. How do these factors affect your life and the lives of people around you? Write each topic in one of the boxes on the left. Then, in the matching box on the right, draw an illustration to show the effects of geography in your area.

Geography in My Area   **Effects of Geography in My Area**

Using what you learned in your reading, write three journal entries dated 1943. Write them from the point of view of either a longtime Detroit resident or a newcomer to the city in 1943.

1. Write a one-paragraph journal entry about your job.

2. Write a one-paragraph journal entry about your daily life at home.

3. Write a one-paragraph journal entry about your community. You could include information about the people you know or information on the surroundings (such as the factories).

Step 1: In each of these years, the average farmer fed this number of people:

1870: 5 people   1920: 10 people   1950: 15 people

On the graph below, use a crayon to fill in the number of people for each of these three years.

Step 2: On the graph below, use a pencil to fill in your predictions for 1960 and for 1970.

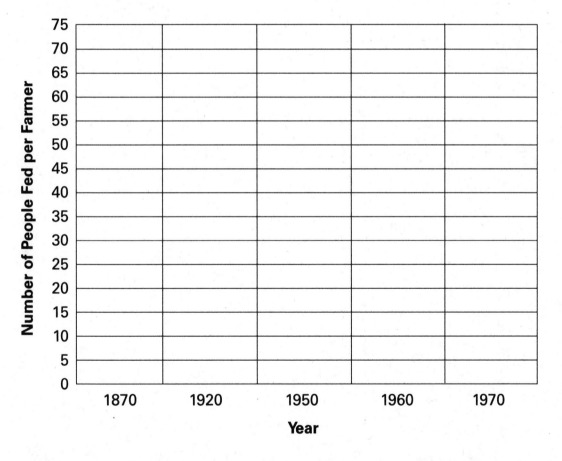

Step 3: In 1960, the average farmer fed 25 people. In 1970, the average farmer fed 75 people. Use a crayon to fill in these figures on your bar graph.

Step 4: Finish this sentence: *I believe one farmer fed more people as the years went by because...*

9

9.2 Below are the beginnings of two bar graphs. Color boxes in the first graph red to show the number of Americans, out of 100, who lived on a farm in 1800. Color boxes in the second graph blue to show the average size of a farm in 1800.

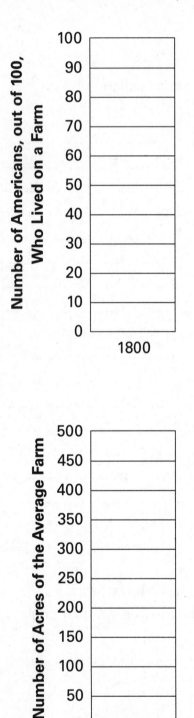

© Teachers' Curriculum Institute

9.3 In the boxes below, draw two tools that farmers used in 1800.

9.4 Write one sentence in each thought bubble to tell about farm life in 1800.

9

9.5 Continue filling in the bar graphs. Copy information from page 54 to fill in the first column of each graph. Then complete the second column of each graph. Color the appropriate number of spaces on the first graph red. Color the appropriate number of spaces on the second graph blue.

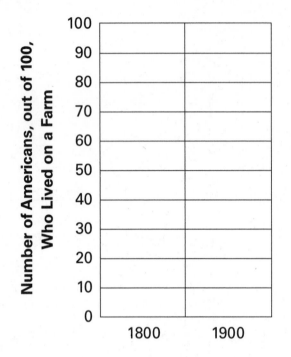

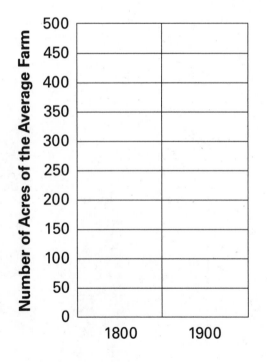

9.6 In the boxes below, draw two tools that farmers used in 1900.

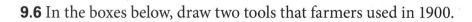

9.7 Write one sentence in each thought bubble to tell about farm life in 1900.

9

9.8 Complete the bar graphs. Copy information from page 56 to fill in the first two columns of each graph. Then complete the third column of each graph. Color the appropriate number of spaces on the first graph red. Color the appropriate number of spaces on the second graph blue.

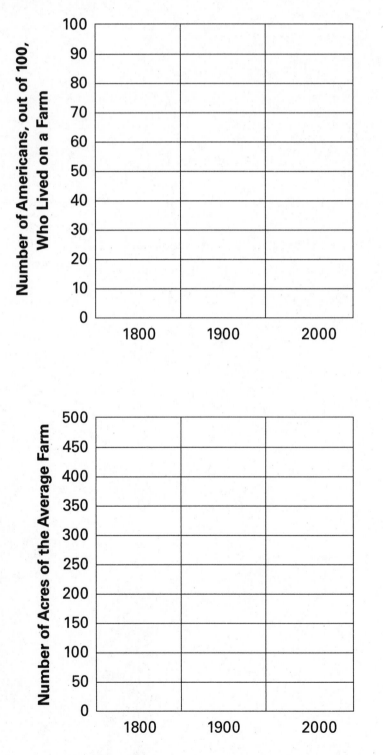

9.9 In the boxes below, draw two tools that farmers used in 2000.

9.10 Write one sentence in each thought bubble to tell about farm life in 2000.

9 You have learned about the many ways in which people today use corn. How might people use corn in the future? Suppose it is 2090. You work for the agency responsible for space flight. Using what you have learned about corn, propose three ideas for using corn to make space travel, or life in space, easier. Write a paragraph describing your ideas in detail.

In each box below, draw one item to show what farming was
like at each point in time.

1800

1900

Today

Examine each of the places shown in the collage of the Southwest. Also look at the map in Section 10.1 of your Student Edition to see the places where the tour will stop. If you could take a trip to any one place in the Southwest, which one would you most want to visit? Why? Write your answer below.

My Southwest Trip

10

Use the spaces below to answer the questions on the Geography Challenge Cards. Write complete sentences. On the map, draw and label the feature that answers each question. Exchange your question with another pair of students until you have completed all the cards.

Question 1.

Question 2.

Question 3.

Question 4.

Question 5.

Question 6.

Question 7.

Question 8.

Question 9.

Question 10.

10

Your class is taking a big rig tour of the Southwest region. The tour will take you to nine locations. As you move from site to site, draw a line on the map to show your route. After visiting each site, draw a symbol or an image at that location to show what you learned there.

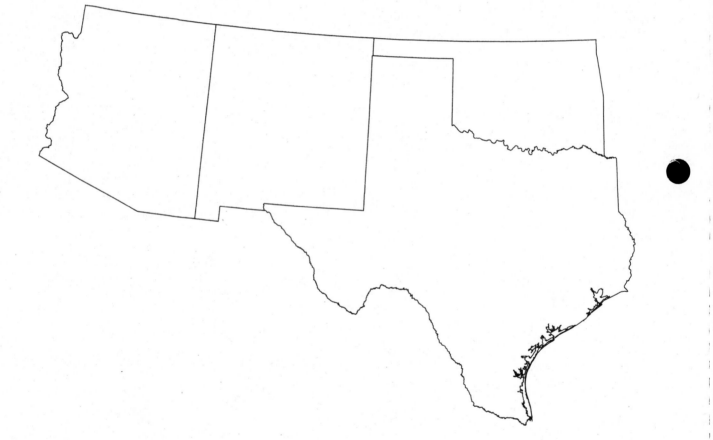

Suppose that you are a newspaper reporter in 1836. You want to write about the Battle of the Alamo that just took place in San Antonio. Answer the questions below. Then use your answers as notes to help you write your article.

Who fought at the Battle of the Alamo?

Why were they fighting?

What details might your readers want to know?

Can you think of a time when there wasn't enough of something for everyone who wanted some? For example, maybe there were 12 children at a birthday party, but only 10 balloons. Write two or three sentences to tell what happened.

Draw a picture of your face that shows how you felt.

Write one sentence telling why you felt that way.

11

Read Section 11.2 in your book. Draw a simple symbol on the map below to show each group of water users. Label each symbol with the name of the group. Then answer the questions below the map.

The Colorado River Basin

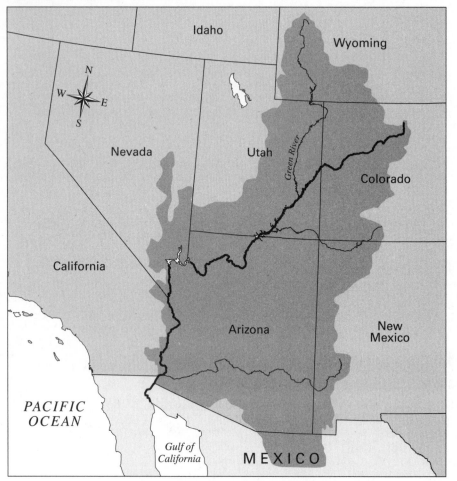

Was there enough water for all the groups of water users in the Colorado River Basin at this time? Why or why not?

If groups had to share the water, how did they do so?

© Teachers' Curriculum Institute

Read Section 11.3 in your book. Then copy all the symbols from your last map onto this one. Next, for each new group of water users, add a simple symbol to the map. Label each symbol with the name of the group. Then answer the questions below the map.

The Colorado River Basin

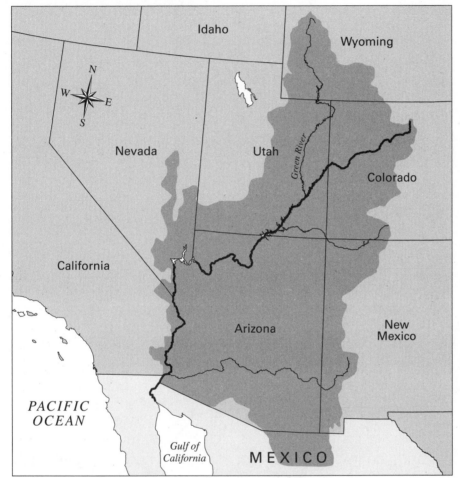

Was there enough water for all the groups of water users in the Colorado River Basin at this time? Why or why not?

If groups had to share the water, how did they do so?

11

Read Sections 11.4 through 11.6 in your book. Then copy all the symbols from your last map onto this one. Next, for each new group of water users, add a simple symbol to the map. Label each symbol with the name of the group. Then answer the questions below the map.

The Colorado River Basin

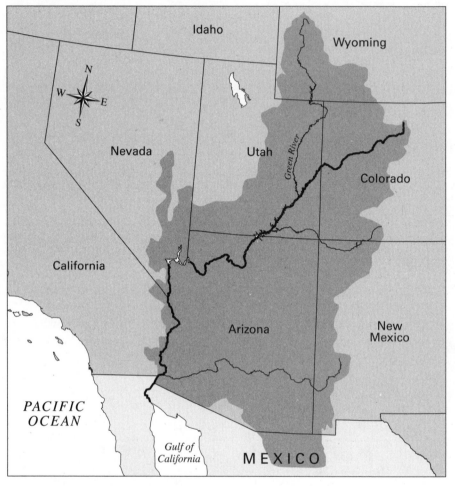

Was there enough water for all the groups of water users in the Colorado River Basin at this time? Why or why not?

If groups had to share the water, how did they do so?

© Teachers' Curriculum Institute

Read Sections 11.7 through 11.10 in your book. Then copy all the symbols from your last map onto this one. Next, for each new group of water users, add a simple symbol to the map. Label each symbol with the name of the group. Then answer the questions below the map.

The Colorado River Basin

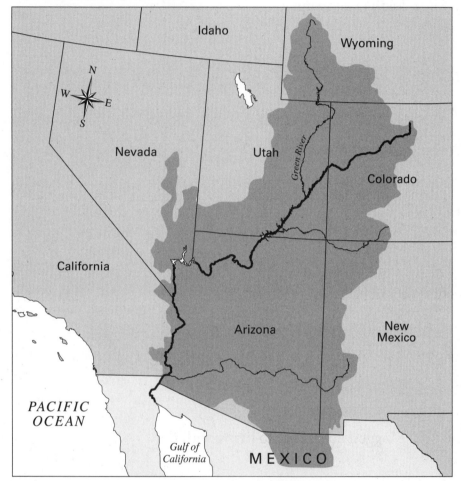

Was there enough water for all the groups of water users in the Colorado River Basin at this time? Why or why not?

If groups had to share the water, how did they do so?

11

Water is a big part of life for the Havasupai people. It helps shape the way they live, work, and have fun in the Grand Canyon. Suppose that you move to Supai, Arizona. Answer the questions below to identify the ways in which water might affect your life there.

1. How might water affect how I will live in Supai?

2. How might water affect how I will work in Supai?

3. How might water affect how I will have fun in Supai?

4. What do you think will be the biggest advantage to living with the water in Supai?

5. What do you think will be the biggest challenge in living with the water in Supai?

Each year, more and more people will need water from the Colorado River. As a result, it will be a challenge in the future to make sure there is enough water for everyone who needs it.

Design a poster for the Southwest that helps people become more aware of this challenge. Your poster design should include these elements:

- a bold, eye-catching illustration
- one sentence that clearly states the challenge
- one sentence that suggests what people can do to help meet the challenge

Examine the images of the West in your textbook. If you could take a trip to the West, what one place in this collage would you most want to visit? Why? Write your answer below.

My Western Trip

12

Use the spaces below to answer the questions on the Geography Challenge Cards. Write complete sentences. Then draw and label the feature that answers each question on the map. Exchange your question with another pair of students until you have completed all the cards.

Question 1.

Question 2.

Question 3.

Question 4.

Question 5.

Question 6.

Question 7.

Question 8.

Question 9.

Question 10.

12

Your class is taking a van and airplane tour of the West region. The tour will take you to nine locations. As you move from site to site, use the map below to keep track of what you learn. After visiting each site, find its location on the map. Draw a symbol or an image to show what you learned there.

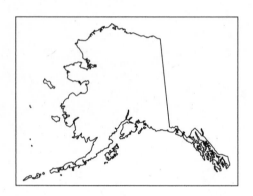

© Teachers' Curriculum Institute

Follow the steps below to plan and create a brochure about the Pacific Crest Trail.

Step 1: Write the name of your group's state.

Step 2: Use books and the Internet to find information about your state's part of the trail.

Step 3: Write five facts about your state's part of the trail.

Step 4: Write two reasons why tourists should visit your state's part of the trail.

Step 5: Write three things tourists might see on your state's part of the trail.

Step 6: With your group, draw pictures of your state's part of the trail on a separate sheet of paper. Use the information you wrote on this paper to write sentences on your brochure.

In the television screen, draw a scene from your favorite commercial. Then answer the questions below.

What does the commercial want the audience to do? For example, does it want people to buy a certain food or toy? Does it want them to see a particular movie?

How does the commercial help the audience remember it? For example, does the commercial use humor or a slogan? Does it feature a famous person?

13

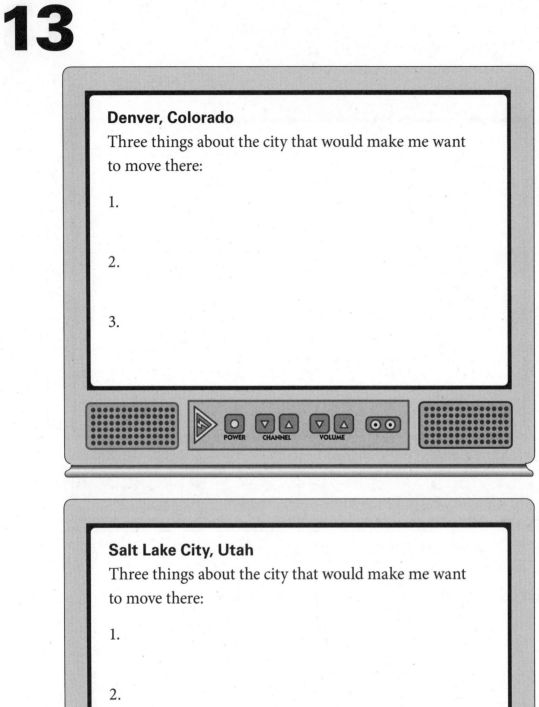

Denver, Colorado

Three things about the city that would make me want to move there:

1.

2.

3.

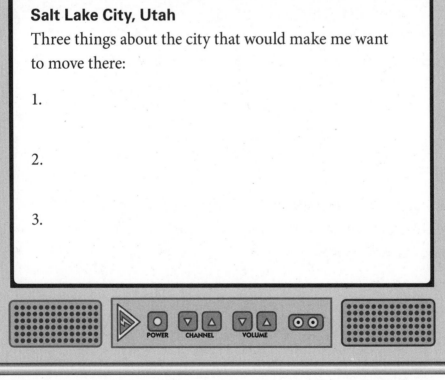

Salt Lake City, Utah

Three things about the city that would make me want to move there:

1.

2.

3.

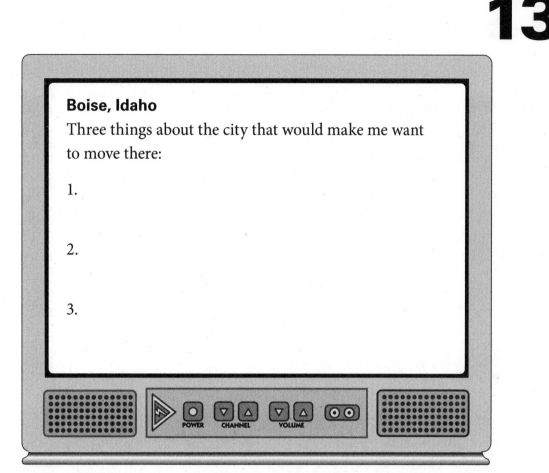

Boise, Idaho

Three things about the city that would make me want to move there:

1.

2.

3.

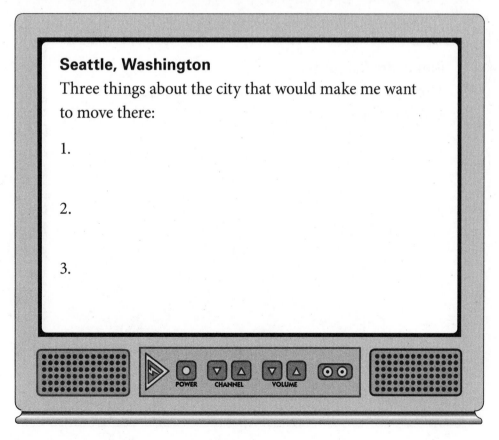

Seattle, Washington

Three things about the city that would make me want to move there:

1.

2.

3.

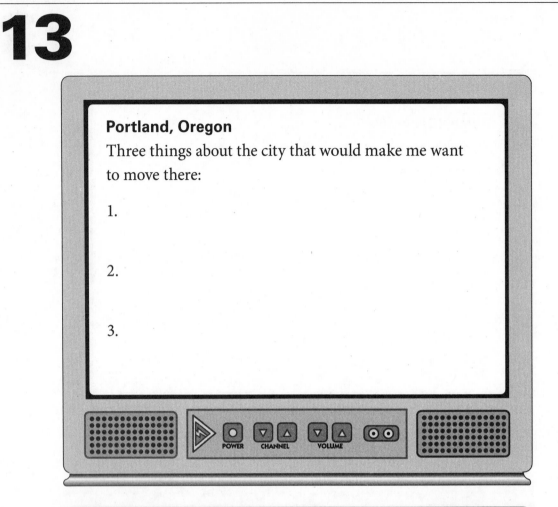

Portland, Oregon

Three things about the city that would make me want to move there:

1.

2.

3.

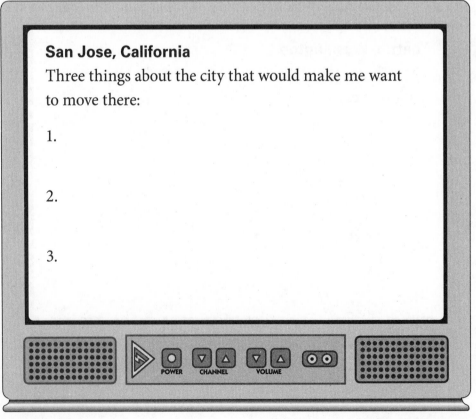

San Jose, California

Three things about the city that would make me want to move there:

1.

2.

3.

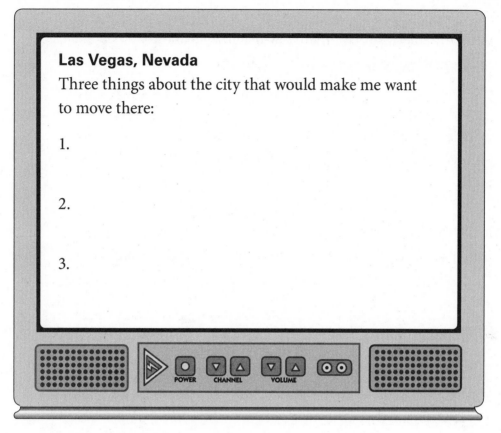

Las Vegas, Nevada

Three things about the city that would make me want to move there:

1.

2.

3.

13

Plan a television commercial about Portland, Oregon.

Step 1: Decide whether your commercial will show Portland as a "green" city or as a "clean" city. Write your choice here:

Step 2: Create a slogan for your commercial that calls attention to the feature you chose above. Write your slogan here:

Step 3: Sketch three pictures for a poster to be used in your commercial. The pictures should relate to the idea in your slogan.

Step 4: Create a sales gimmick for your commercial. The gimmick should call attention to how Portland is a "green" city or a "clean" city. Describe your sales gimmick here:

Step 5: Describe what will happen in your commercial, step by step. Be sure to mention how you will use the poster and the gimmick.

13

Use the Venn diagram below to compare the community where you live to the city of the West that you like best.

First, write the names of the two communities on the lines.

Next, in the area where the two circles overlap, write two things that are similar about these communities.

Last, in the areas where the two circles do not overlap, write two things that are different about these communities.

Community where I live: **City of the West that I like best:**

_____   _____

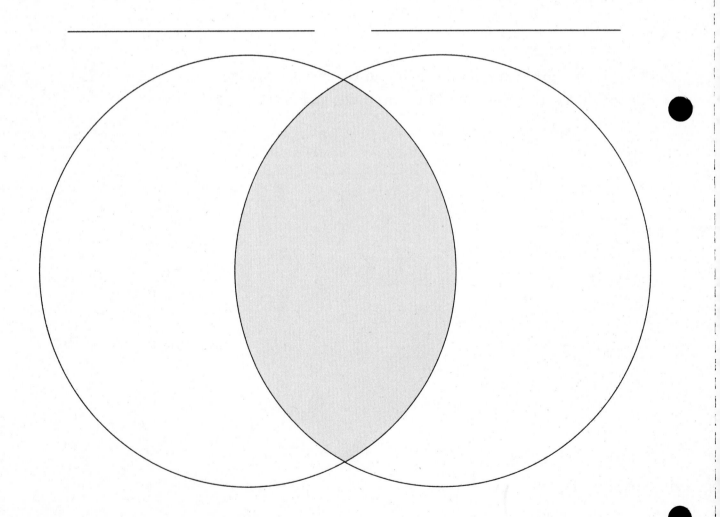

Part 1

Think of all of the board games you have played. Name your favorite one.

List three reasons this game is fun to play.

1.

2.

3.

Part 2

Suppose you are creating a board game about people's knowledge of your state's geography. What key features—such as cities, rivers, mountains, or landmarks—would you include? List at least five features below.

1.

2.

3.

4.

5.

14

Read Sections 14.2 through 14.6, and record notes below.

14.2 What tools do geographers use to study a state's geography?

14.3 How might geography have helped shape a state's history?

14.4 How might geography have helped shape a state's economy?

14

14.5 What are six sources people can use to research their state's geography?

1.

2.

3.

4.

5.

6.

14.6 What are the five steps of the geographic inquiry process?

Step 1.

Step 2.

Step 3.

Step 4.

Step 5.

14

Carefully examine the objects your teacher has displayed. Choose three objects that you think would tell archaeologists in the future the most about the geography of where you live. Then answer the questions below.

Object 1

• What is the object?

• Why did you choose this object? What might this object show future archaeologists about where you live? Explain your reasons in detail.

Object 2

• What is the object?

• Why did you choose this object? What might this object show future archaeologists about where you live? Explain your reasons in detail.

Object 3

• What is the object?

• Why did you choose this object? What might this object show future archaeologists about where you live? Explain your reasons in detail.

Play your board game with your family or with several students in a lower grade. Afterward, ask players the following questions. Record their answers.

1. Did you enjoy playing the game? Why or why not?

2. What did you learn about our state's geography by playing the game?

Then answer the following questions yourself.

3. How successful do you think your board game is as a tool to teach the geography of your state?

4. Is there anything you would change about your board game now? Why or why not?

Think of all the buildings you have seen in your state. In the left column below, draw simple sketches of the three kinds of buildings that are most familiar to you. In the right column, sketch three specific buildings that you think are the most famous. Try to choose buildings from different time periods.

Three Familiar Building Types	Three Famous Buildings

15

Read Sections 15.2 through 15.7, and record notes below.

15.2 How do historians explore the past?

-
-
-

15.3 Why do people study history?

-
-
-

15.4 How were most of our states settled?

-

-

15.5 What are three ways that states became part of the United States?

-

-

-

15.6 What drew people to some of the states?

-

-

15.7 What things influence a state's growth and development?

-

-

15

As you read about the President's House, record at least three questions that Ed Lawler asked during his research.

1.

2.

3.

After reading, record at least three questions that you would ask about the President's House.

1.

2.

3.

Part 1

Think of the many jobs people do in your state. Consider people like your parents, your neighbors, the people who work at the local grocery store, and even your teacher. What do you think are popular jobs in your state? Fill in the table below.

Three Popular Jobs	What Do People Do at These Jobs?

Part 2

List eight important economic activities in your state.

$ Michigan

1.

2.

3.

4.

5.

6.

7.

8.

16

Read Sections 16.2 through 16.7 in your book and complete the notes below.

16.2 What are the three basic economic questions that people, businesses, and governments seek to answer?

1.

2.

3.

16.3 How does an economist define the word *market*?

16.4 List the three factors of production.

1.

2.

3.

© Teachers' Curriculum Institute

16.5 List two things consumers can do to use their money wisely.

1.

2.

16.6 What are two things that help shape the way an economy grows and develops?

1.

2.

16.7 List five economic activities that are common in the United States.

1.

2.

3.

4.

5.

16

Think about things you do at home, in school, and in the community. Then answer the questions below.

1. What experiences have you had that taught you about real-world work? Describe your experiences.

2. Choose one experience. Explain what the experience taught you about real-world work.

Complete items A, B, and C below to summarize what you have learned about the economies of your state and your community.

A. List three differences between the economy of your state and the economy of your community.

1.

2.

3.

B. List two similarities between the economy of your state and the economy of your community.

1.

2.

C. Write one question you still have about the economy of your state or the economy of your community.

Part 1 Laws are made to help solve problems. The first step in creating a law is identifying a problem. What problems do you see in your community or state? Work with your partner to create a list of four problems you would like to see solved.

1.

2.

3.

4.

Part 2 In the space below, record other problems suggested by your classmates.

17

Part 3 After a problem has been identified, the next step is to propose a solution. Suppose that your state has the problems listed below. Work with your partner to think of creative solutions to each problem. Record your ideas, and be ready to share them.

Problem	Possible Solutions
Several cities in your state suffer from air pollution.	
Many public schools in your state are overcrowded.	
Drivers using cellular phones have caused many car accidents in your state.	

17

Read Sections 17.2 through 17.7 and record answers to the questions below.

17.2 Who shares power in a federal system of government?

17.3 What are the three branches of government, and what does each branch do?

17.4 Why are leaders important in a republic?

17.5 How do we choose our leaders?

17.6 How does an idea become a state law?

17.7 Give one or more examples of citizen rights. Give one or more examples of citizen responsibilities.

17

Part 1

With your group, research and list four of your state's symbols.

1.

2.

3.

4.

Part 2

Brainstorm four ideas for new state symbols. For example, you could suggest that the state have a state pet, and you could propose that it be the golden retriever. For each symbol, explain why you think this would be a good symbol for your state.

1.

2.

3.

4.

Photographs

Cover
David Olsen/Getty Images

Title Page
David Olsen/Getty Images

Art

2: Rosiland Solomon **3:** Rosiland Solomon **5 R:** Rosiland Solomon **5 B:** Doug Roy **14 C:** Susan Jaekel **14 TR:** Doug Roy **14 BR:** Renate Lohmann **14 TL:** Siri Weber Feeney **14 BL:** Len Ebert **21:** Doug Roy **22:** DJ Simison **24:** DJ Simison **28:** Doug Roy **29:** Doug Roy **30:** Doug Roy **33:** Doug Roy **34:** DJ Simison **36:** DJ Simison **39:** Doug Roy **40:** Doug Roy **42:** Doug Roy **47:** Doug Roy **48:** DJ Simison **50:** DJ Simison **51:** Doug Roy **55:** DJ Simison **57:** DJ Simison **59:** DJ Simison **60:** Jon Goodell **63:** Doug Roy **64:** DJ Simison **66:** DJ Simison **77:** Doug Roy **78:** DJ Simison **80:** DJ Simison **92:** Doug Roy **98:** Doug Roy **102:** Gary Undercuffler

Artists represented by Ann Remen-Willis,
Artist Representative and Art Manager:
Len Ebert
Jon Goodell
Susan Jaekel
Renate Lohmann
Doug Roy
DJ Simison
Rosiland Solomon
Gary Undercuffler
Siri Weber Feeney

Michigan Job Choice

1. What Michigan job would you do?

2. Why?

3. What would some of your duties be?

4. Detailed Picture